A SHORT TABLE
OF INTEGRALS

BY

B. O. PEIRCE

HOLLIS PROFESSOR OF MATHEMATICS AND NATURAL PHILOSOPHY
IN HARVARD UNIVERSITY

THIRD REVISED EDITION

GINN AND COMPANY

BOSTON · NEW YORK · CHICAGO · LONDON
ATLANTA · DALLAS · COLUMBUS · SAN FRANCISCO

The Athenæum Press

GINN AND COMPANY · PRO-
PRIETORS · BOSTON · U.S.A.

TABLE OF INTEGRALS.

PRINCIPAL VALUES.

In the following tables the inverse trigonometric functions are to be understood as restricted to their *principal values*. These are indicated by the accompanying figures.

$y = \sin^{-1}x.$ $y = \cos^{-1}x.$

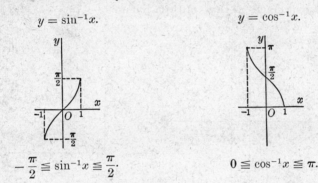

$$-\frac{\pi}{2} \leqq \sin^{-1}x \leqq \frac{\pi}{2}.$$ $$0 \leqq \cos^{-1}x \leqq \pi.$$

The curves representing the functions $\tan^{-1}x$ and $\text{ctn}^{-1}x$ extend indefinitely in both directions.

$y = \tan^{-1}x.$

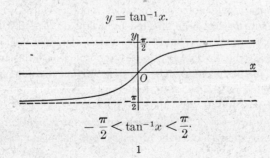

$$-\frac{\pi}{2} < \tan^{-1}x < \frac{\pi}{2}.$$

1

The principal value of $\operatorname{ctn}^{-1}x$ is connected with the principal value of $\tan^{-1}x$ by the relation $\tan^{-1}x + \operatorname{ctn}^{-1}x = \frac{1}{2}\pi$.

$$y = \operatorname{ctn}^{-1}x.$$

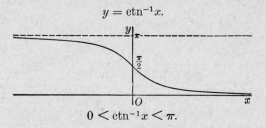

$$0 < \operatorname{ctn}^{-1}x < \pi.$$

The tables are adapted to the use of the hyperbolic functions, and graphs of three of them follow.

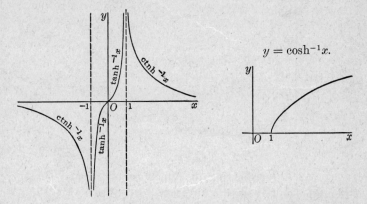

$$y = \cosh^{-1}x.$$

In certain trigonometric formulas, notably those in which the integration has been effected by means of the substitution $z = \tan \frac{1}{2}x$, there is a hidden use of the principal value, over and above the principal value of the function occurring explicitly in the formula, and so restrictions on the independent variable are necessary. See, for example, Formula 300.

Formulas 49, 50, 298, and 300 have been recast to the end that they be correct for all values of a, b for which they have a meaning, that they cover all cases, and that they be better adapted to computation. Only one formula, 316, has been dropped, as being both incomplete and unnecessary; and the numbering of the formulas has been retained except in the case of Formulas 314–316.

The formula

$$\log (x + yi) = \tfrac{1}{2} \log (x^2 + y^2) + i \tan^{-1} \frac{y}{x}$$

is treacherous, since the values of the multiple-valued function on the left cannot be expressed in terms of the principal value of $\tan^{-1} y/x$, $\pm k\pi$. Sometimes an even multiple of π must be added, and sometimes an odd multiple.

The formula which is correct in all cases is the following:

$$\log (x + yi) = \log r + \phi i,$$
$$x = r \cos \phi, \quad y = r \sin \phi, \quad r = \sqrt{x^2 + y^2}.$$

The tables of tabulated functions remain as in the earlier edition, except that the pages of hyperbolic functions have been revised and a table of square roots has been added.

I. FUNDAMENTAL FORMS.

1. $\int a \, dx = ax.$

2. $\int af(x) \, dx = a \int f(x) \, dx.$

3. $\int \frac{dx}{x} = \log x.$ $\quad [\log x = \log (-x) + (2k + 1)\pi i.]$

4. $\int x^m dx = \frac{x^{m+1}}{m+1},$ when m is different from -1.

5. $\int e^x dx = e^x.$

6. $\int a^x \log a \, dx = a^x.$

7. $\displaystyle\int \frac{dx}{1 + x^2} = \tan^{-1}x, \text{ or } - \operatorname{ctn}^{-1}x.$

8. $\displaystyle\int \frac{dx}{\sqrt{1 - x^2}} = \sin^{-1}x, \text{ or } - \cos^{-1}x.$

9. $\displaystyle\int \frac{dx}{x\sqrt{x^2 - 1}} = \sec^{-1}x, \text{ or } - \csc^{-1}x.$

10. $\displaystyle\int \frac{dx}{\sqrt{2\,x - x^2}} = \operatorname{versin}^{-1}x, \text{ or } - \operatorname{coversin}^{-1}x.$

11. $\displaystyle\int \cos x \, dx = \sin x, \text{ or } - \operatorname{coversin} x.$

12. $\displaystyle\int \sin x \, dx = - \cos x, \text{ or } \operatorname{versin} x.$

13. $\displaystyle\int \operatorname{ctn} x \, dx = \log \sin x.$

14. $\displaystyle\int \tan x \, dx = - \log \cos x.$

15. $\displaystyle\int \tan x \sec x \, dx = \sec x.$

16. $\displaystyle\int \sec^2 x \, dx = \tan x.$

17. $\displaystyle\int \csc^2 x \, dx = - \operatorname{ctn} x.$

In the following formulas, u, v, w, and y represent any functions of x:

18. $\displaystyle\int (u + v + w + \text{etc.}) \, dx = \int u \, dx + \int v \, dx + \int w \, dx + \text{etc.}$

19 a. $\displaystyle\int u \, dv = uv - \int v \, du.$

19 b. $\displaystyle\int u \frac{dv}{dx} \, dx = uv - \int v \frac{du}{dx} \, dx.$

20. $\displaystyle\int f(y) \, dx = \int \frac{f(y) \, dy}{\dfrac{dy}{dx}}.$

II. RATIONAL ALGEBRAIC FUNCTIONS.

A. — EXPRESSIONS INVOLVING $(a + bx)$.

The substitution of y or z for x, where $y \equiv a + bx$, $z \equiv (a + bx) / x$, gives

21. $\displaystyle\int (a + bx)^m dx = \frac{1}{b} \int y^m dy.$

22. $\displaystyle\int x (a + bx)^m dx = \frac{1}{b^2} \int y^m (y - a) \, dy.$

23. $\displaystyle\int x^n (a + bx)^m dx = \frac{1}{b^{n+1}} \int y^m (y - a)^n \, dy.$

24. $\displaystyle\int \frac{x^n dx}{(a + bx)^m} = \frac{1}{b^{n+1}} \int \frac{(y - a)^n dy}{y^m}.$

25. $\displaystyle\int \frac{dx}{x^n (a + bx)^m} = -\frac{1}{a^{m+n-1}} \int \frac{(z - b)^{m+n-2} dz}{z^m}.$

Whence

26. $\displaystyle\int \frac{dx}{a + bx} = \frac{1}{b} \log (a + bx).$

27. $\displaystyle\int \frac{dx}{(a + bx)^2} = -\frac{1}{b (a + bx)}.$

28. $\displaystyle\int \frac{dx}{(a + bx)^3} = -\frac{1}{2 b (a + bx)^2}.$

29. $\displaystyle\int \frac{x \, dx}{a + bx} = \frac{1}{b^2} [a + bx - a \log (a + bx)].$

30. $\displaystyle\int \frac{x \, dx}{(a + bx)^2} = \frac{1}{b^2} \left[\log (a + bx) + \frac{a}{a + bx} \right].$

31. $\displaystyle\int \frac{x\,dx}{(a+bx)^3} = \frac{1}{b^2}\left[-\frac{1}{a+bx} + \frac{a}{2(a+bx)^2}\right].$

32. $\displaystyle\int \frac{x^2\,dx}{a+bx} = \frac{1}{b^3}\left[\tfrac{1}{2}(a+bx)^2 - 2a(a+bx) + a^2\log(a+bx)\right].$

33. $\displaystyle\int \frac{x^2\,dx}{(a+bx)^2} = \frac{1}{b^3}\left[a+bx-2a\log(a+bx)-\frac{a^2}{a+bx}\right].$

34. $\displaystyle\int \frac{dx}{x\,(a+bx)} = -\frac{1}{a}\log\frac{a+bx}{x}.$ *

35. $\displaystyle\int \frac{dx}{x(a+bx)^2} = \frac{1}{a(a+bx)} - \frac{1}{a^2}\log\frac{a+bx}{x}.$

36. $\displaystyle\int \frac{(a+bx)\,dx}{a'+b'x} = \frac{bx}{b'} + \frac{ab'-a'b}{b'^2}\log(a'+b'x).$

37. $\displaystyle\int (a+bx)^n (a'+b'x)^m\,dx = \frac{1}{(m+n+1)\,b}\Big((a+bx)^{n+1}(a'+b'x)^m$
$$-\,m\,(ab'-a'b)\int (a+bx)^n (a'+b'x)^{m-1}\,dx\Big).$$

38. $\displaystyle\int \frac{(a+bx)^n\,dx}{(a'+b'x)^m} = -\frac{1}{(m-1)(ab'-a'b)}\left(\frac{(a+bx)^{n+1}}{(a'+b'x)^{m-1}}\right.$
$$\left.+\,(m-n-2)\,b\int\frac{(a+bx)^n\,dx}{(a'+b'x)^{m-1}}\right)$$
$$=-\frac{1}{(m-n-1)\,b'}\left(\frac{(a+bx)^n}{(a'+b'x)^{m-1}}\right.$$
$$\left.+\,n\,(ab'-a'b)\int\frac{(a+bx)^{n-1}\,dx}{(a'+b'x)^m}\right)$$
$$=-\frac{1}{(m-1)\,b'}\left(\frac{(a+bx)^n}{(a'+b'x)^{m-1}}-nb\int\frac{(a+bx)^{n-1}\,dx}{(a'+b'x)^{m-1}}\right).$$

$\displaystyle *\int \frac{dx}{x^2(a+bx)} = -\frac{1}{ax} + \frac{b}{a^2}\log\frac{a+bx}{x}.$

39. $\displaystyle\int \frac{dx}{(a + bx)\,(a' + b'x)} = \frac{1}{ab' - a'b} \cdot \log \frac{a' + b'x}{a + bx}.$

40. $\displaystyle\int \frac{dx}{(a + bx)^n\,(a' + b'x)^m}$

$$= \frac{1}{(m-1)\,(ab' - a'b)} \left(\frac{-1}{(a + bx)^{n-1}\,(a' + b'x)^{m-1}} \right.$$
$$\left. - (m + n - 2)\,b \int \frac{dx}{(a + bx)^n\,(a' + b'x)^{m-1}} \right).$$

41. $\displaystyle\int \frac{x\,dx}{(a + bx)\,(a' + b'x)}$

$$= \frac{1}{ab' - a'b} \left(\frac{a}{b} \log\,(a + bx) - \frac{a'}{b'} \log\,(a' + b'x) \right).$$

42. $\displaystyle\int \frac{dx}{(a + bx)^2(a' + b'x)}$

$$= \frac{1}{ab' - a'b} \left(\frac{1}{a + bx} + \frac{b'}{ab' - a'b} \log \frac{a' + b'x}{a + bx} \right).$$

43. $\displaystyle\int \frac{x\,dx}{(a + bx)^2\,(a' + b'x)}$

$$= \frac{-a}{b\,(ab' - a'b)\,(a + bx)} - \frac{a'}{(ab' - a'b)^2} \log \frac{a' + b'x}{a + bx}.$$

44. $\displaystyle\int \frac{x^2\,dx}{(a + bx)^2\,(a' + b'x)} = \frac{a^2}{b^2\,(ab' - a'b)\,(a + bx)}$

$$+ \frac{1}{(ab' - a'b)^2} \left[\frac{a'^2}{b'} \log\,(a' + b'x) + \frac{a\,(ab' - 2\,a'b)}{b^2} \log\,(a + bx) \right].$$

45. $\displaystyle\int (a + bx)^{\frac{1}{n}}\,dx = \frac{n}{(n + 1)\,b}\,(a + bx)^{\frac{n+1}{n}}.$

46. $\displaystyle\int \frac{dx}{(a + bx)^{\frac{1}{n}}} = \frac{n}{(n - 1)\,b}\,(a + bx)^{\frac{n-1}{n}},$

B. — Expressions Involving $(a + bx^n)$.

47. $\displaystyle\int \frac{dx}{c^2 + x^2} = \frac{1}{c}\tan^{-1}\frac{x}{c} = \frac{1}{c}\sin^{-1}\frac{x}{\sqrt{x^2 + c^2}}.$

48. $\displaystyle\int \frac{dx}{c^2 - x^2} = \frac{1}{2\,c}\log\frac{c + x}{c - x} = \frac{1}{c}\tanh^{-1}\frac{x}{c},$ or $\frac{1}{c}\operatorname{ctnh}^{-1}\frac{x}{c}.$

49. $\displaystyle\int \frac{dx}{a + bx^2} = \frac{1}{\sqrt{ab}}\tan^{-1}\frac{x\sqrt{ab}}{a}.$

50. $\displaystyle\int \frac{dx}{a + bx^2} = \frac{1}{2\sqrt{-ab}}\log\frac{a + x\sqrt{-ab}}{a - x\sqrt{-ab}},$

or $\dfrac{1}{\sqrt{-ab}}\tanh^{-1}\dfrac{x\sqrt{-ab}}{a},$ or $\dfrac{1}{\sqrt{-ab}}\operatorname{ctnh}^{-1}\dfrac{x\sqrt{-ab}}{a}.$

51. $\displaystyle\int \frac{dx}{(a + bx^2)^2} = \frac{x}{2\,a(a + bx^2)} + \frac{1}{2\,a}\int \frac{dx}{a + bx^2}.$

52. $\displaystyle\int \frac{dx}{(a + bx^2)^{m+1}} = \frac{1}{2\,ma}\cdot\frac{x}{(a + bx^2)^m} + \frac{2\,m - 1}{2\,ma}\int \frac{dx}{(a + bx^2)^m}.$

53. $\displaystyle\int \frac{x\,dx}{a + bx^2} = \frac{1}{2\,b}\log\left(x^2 + \frac{a}{b}\right).$

54. $\displaystyle\int \frac{x\,dx}{(a + bx^2)^{m+1}} = \frac{1}{2}\int \frac{dz}{(a + bz)^{m+1}},$ where $z = x^2.$

55. $\displaystyle\int \frac{dx}{x(a + bx^2)} = \frac{1}{2\,a}\log\frac{x^2}{a + bx^2}.$

56. $\displaystyle\int \frac{x^2\,dx}{a + bx^2} = \frac{x}{b} - \frac{a}{b}\int \frac{dx}{a + bx^2}.$

57. $\displaystyle\int \frac{dx}{x^2(a + bx^2)} = -\frac{1}{ax} - \frac{b}{a}\int \frac{dx}{a + bx^2}.$

58. $\displaystyle\int \frac{x^2\,dx}{(a + bx^2)^{m+1}} = \frac{-x}{2\,mb\,(a + bx^2)^m} + \frac{1}{2\,mb}\int \frac{dx}{(a + bx^2)^m}.$

59. $\displaystyle\int \frac{dx}{x^2(a + bx^2)^{m+1}} = \frac{1}{a}\int \frac{dx}{x^2(a + bx^2)^m} - \frac{b}{a}\int \frac{dx}{(a + bx^2)^{m+1}}.$

60. $\displaystyle\int \frac{dx}{a+bx^3} = \frac{k}{3\,a}\left[\tfrac{1}{2}\log\left(\frac{(k+x)^2}{k^2-kx+x^2}\right) + \sqrt{3}\tan^{-1}\frac{2x-k}{k\sqrt{3}}\right]$, where $bk^3 = a.$

61. $\displaystyle\int \frac{x\,dx}{a+bx^3} = \frac{1}{3bk}\left[\tfrac{1}{2}\log\left(\frac{k^2-kx+x^2}{(k+x)^2}\right) + \sqrt{3}\tan^{-1}\frac{2x-k}{k\sqrt{3}}\right]$, where $bk^3 = a.$

62. $\displaystyle\int \frac{dx}{x(a+bx^n)} = \frac{1}{an}\log\frac{x^n}{a+bx^n}.$

63. $\displaystyle\int \frac{dx}{(a+bx^n)^{m+1}} = \frac{1}{a}\int\frac{dx}{(a+bx^n)^m} - \frac{b}{a}\int\frac{x^n\,dx}{(a+bx^n)^{m+1}}.$

64. $\displaystyle\int \frac{x^m\,dx}{(a+bx^n)^{p+1}} = \frac{1}{b}\int\frac{x^{m-n}\,dx}{(a+bx^n)^p} - \frac{a}{b}\int\frac{x^{m-n}\,dx}{(a+bx^n)^{p+1}}.$

65. $\displaystyle\int \frac{dx}{x^m(a+bx^n)^{p+1}} = \frac{1}{a}\int\frac{dx}{x^m(a+bx^n)^p} - \frac{b}{a}\int\frac{dx}{x^{m-n}(a+bx^n)^{p+1}}.$

66. $\displaystyle\int x^{m-1}(a+bx^n)^p\,dx =$

$\displaystyle\frac{1}{b(m+np)}\left[x^{m-n}(a+bx^n)^{p+1} - (m-n)a\int x^{m-n-1}(a+bx^n)^p\,dx\right].$

$\displaystyle\frac{1}{m+np}\left[x^m(a+bx^n)^p + npa\int x^{m-1}(a+bx^n)^{p-1}\,dx\right].$

$\displaystyle\frac{1}{ma}\left[x^m(a+bx^n)^{p+1} - (m+np+n)b\int x^{m+n-1}(a+bx^n)^p\,dx\right].$

$\displaystyle\frac{1}{an(p+1)}\left[-x^m(a+bx^n)^{p+1} + (m+np+n)\int x^{m-1}(a+bx^n)^{p+1}\,dx\right].$

C. — Expressions Involving $(a + bx + cx^2)$.

Let $X = a + bx + cx^2$ and $q = 4\,ac - b^2$, then

67. $\displaystyle \int \frac{dx}{X} = \frac{2}{\sqrt{q}}\,\tan^{-1}\frac{2\,cx + b}{\sqrt{q}}.$

68. $\displaystyle \int \frac{dx}{X} = \frac{1}{\sqrt{-q}}\,\log\frac{2\,cx + b - \sqrt{-q}}{2\,cx + b + \sqrt{-q}},$

$\displaystyle \text{or } \frac{-2}{\sqrt{-q}}\,\tanh^{-1}\frac{2\,cx + b}{\sqrt{-q}},\ \text{ or }\ \frac{-2}{\sqrt{-q}}\,\text{ctnh}^{-1}\frac{2\,cx + b}{\sqrt{-q}}$

69. $\displaystyle \int \frac{dx}{X^2} = \frac{2\,cx + b}{qX} + \frac{2\,c}{q}\int \frac{dx}{X}.$

70. $\displaystyle \int \frac{dx}{X^3} = \frac{2\,cx + b}{q}\left(\frac{1}{2\,X^2} + \frac{3\,c}{qX}\right) + \frac{6\,c^2}{q^2}\int \frac{dx}{X}.$

71. $\displaystyle \int \frac{dx}{X^{n+1}} = \frac{2\,cx + b}{nqX^n} + \frac{2(2\,n - 1)\,c}{qn}\int \frac{dx}{X^n}.$

72. $\displaystyle \int \frac{x\,dx}{X} = \frac{1}{2\,c}\,\log X - \frac{b}{2\,c}\int \frac{dx}{X}.$

73. $\displaystyle \int \frac{x\,dx}{X^2} = -\frac{bx + 2\,a}{qX} - \frac{b}{q}\int \frac{dx}{X}.$

74. $\displaystyle \int \frac{x\,dx}{X^{n+1}} = -\frac{2\,a + bx}{nqX^n} - \frac{b\,(2\,n - 1)}{nq}\int \frac{dx}{X^n}.$

75. $\displaystyle \int \frac{x^2}{X}\,dx = \frac{x}{c} - \frac{b}{2\,c^2}\,\log X + \frac{b^2 - 2\,ac}{2\,c^2}\int \frac{dx}{X}.$

76. $\displaystyle \int \frac{x^2}{X^2}\,dx = \frac{(b^2 - 2\,ac)\,x + ab}{cqX} + \frac{2\,a}{q}\int \frac{dx}{X}.$

77. $\displaystyle \int \frac{x^m\,dx}{X^{n+1}} = -\frac{x^{m-1}}{(2\,n - m + 1)\,cX^n} - \frac{n - m + 1}{2\,n - m + 1}\cdot\frac{b}{c}\int \frac{x^{m-1}\,dx}{X^{n+1}}$
$\displaystyle \qquad\qquad + \frac{m - 1}{2\,n - m + 1}\cdot\frac{a}{c}\int \frac{x^{m-2}\,dx}{X^{n+1}}.$

78. $\int \dfrac{dx}{xX} = \dfrac{1}{2\,a} \log \dfrac{x^2}{X} - \dfrac{b}{2\,a} \int \dfrac{dx}{X}.$

79. $\int \dfrac{dx}{x^2 X} = \dfrac{b}{2\,a^2} \log \dfrac{X}{x^2} - \dfrac{1}{ax} + \left(\dfrac{b^2}{2\,a^2} - \dfrac{c}{a} \right) \int \dfrac{dx}{X}.$

80. $\int \dfrac{dx}{x^m X^{n+1}} = -\dfrac{1}{(m-1)\,ax^{m-1}X^n} - \dfrac{n+m-1}{m-1} \cdot \dfrac{b}{a} \int \dfrac{dx}{x^{m-1}X^{n+1}}$

$$- \dfrac{2\,n+m-1}{m-1} \cdot \dfrac{c}{a} \int \dfrac{dx}{x^{m-2}X^{n+1}}.$$

81. $\int X^n\, dx = \dfrac{1}{2\,(2\,n+1)\,c} \left((b+2\,cx)\,X^n + nq \int X^{n-1}\, dx \right).$

82. $\int \dfrac{dx}{x\,X^n} = \dfrac{1}{2\,a\,(n-1)\,X^{n-1}} - \dfrac{b}{2\,a} \int \dfrac{dx}{X^n} + \dfrac{1}{a} \int \dfrac{dx}{x\,X^{n-1}}.$

83. $\int \dfrac{dx}{(a'+b'x)\,X} = \dfrac{1}{2\,(ab'^2 - a'bb' + a'^2c)} \left(b'\,(\log\,(a'+b'x)^2 \right.$

$$\left. - \log X) + (2\,a'c - bb') \int \dfrac{dx}{X} \right).$$

84. $\int (a'+b'x)\,X^n\, dx = \dfrac{b'X^{n+1}}{2\,(n+1)\,c} + \dfrac{2\,a'c - bb'}{2\,c} \int X^n\, dx.$

85. $\int \dfrac{(a'+b'x)\,dx}{X^n} = -\dfrac{b'}{2\,(n-1)\,c\,X^{n-1}} + \dfrac{2\,a'c - bb'}{2\,c} \int \dfrac{dx}{X^n}.$

86. $\int (a'+b'x)^m\,X^n\, dx = \dfrac{1}{(m+2\,n+1)\,c} \left(b'(a'+b'x)^{m-1}X^{n+1} \right.$

$$+ (m+n)(2\,a'c - bb') \int (a'+b'x)^{m-1}X^n\, dx$$

$$\left. - (m-1)(ab'^2 - a'bb' + ca'^2) \int (a'+b'x)^{m-2}X^n\, dx \right).$$

87. $\displaystyle\int \frac{(a' + b'x)^m \, dx}{X^n} = \frac{1}{q\,(n-1)} \left(\frac{(b + 2\,cx)(a' + b'x)^m}{X^{n-1}} \right.$

$$- 2\,(m - 2\,n + 3)\,c \int \frac{(a' + b'x)^m \, dx}{X^{n-1}}$$

$$\left. + m\,(2\,a'c - bb') \int \frac{(a' + b'x)^{m-1} \, dx}{X^{n-1}} \right)$$

$$= \frac{1}{(m - 2\,n + 1)\,c} \left(\frac{b'\,(a' + b'x)^{m-1}}{X^{n-1}}. \right.$$

$$+ (m - n)\,(2\,a'c - bb') \int \frac{(a' + b'x)^{m-1} \, dx}{X^n}$$

$$\left. - (m - 1)\,(ab'^2 - a'bb' + ca'^2) \int \frac{(a' + b'x)^{m-2} \, dx}{X^n} \right)$$

88. $\displaystyle\int \frac{X^n \, dx}{(a' + b'x)^m}$

$$= \frac{1}{b'^2\,(m-1)} \left(\frac{- b'X^n}{(a' + b'x)^{m-1}} \right.$$

$$+ n\,(bb' - 2\,a'c) \int \frac{X^{n-1} \, dx}{(a' + b'x)^{\,m-1}}$$

$$\left. + 2\,nc \int \frac{X^{n-1} \, dx}{(a' + b'x)^{m-2}} \right)$$

$$= - \frac{1}{(m - 2\,n - 1)\,b'^2} \left(\frac{+ b'X^n}{(a' + b'x)^{m-1}} \right.$$

$$+ 2\,n\,(ab'^2 - a'bb' + ca'^2) \int \frac{X^{n-1} \, dx}{(a' + b'x)^m}$$

$$\left. + n\,(bb' - 2\,a'c) \int \frac{X^{n-1} \, dx}{(a' + b'x)^{m-1}} \right).$$

III. IRRATIONAL ALGEBRAIC FUNCTIONS.

A. — Expressions Involving $\sqrt{a + bx}$.

The substitution of a new variable of integration, $y = \sqrt{a + bx}$, gives

91. $\displaystyle \int \sqrt{a + bx}\, dx = \frac{2}{3\,b} \sqrt{(a + bx)^3}.$

92. $\displaystyle \int x \sqrt{a + bx}\, dx = -\frac{2(2\,a - 3\,bx) \sqrt{(a + bx)^3}}{15\,b^2}.$

93. $\displaystyle \int x^2 \sqrt{a + bx}\, dx = \frac{2(8\,a^2 - 12\,abx + 15\,b^2x^2) \sqrt{(a + bx)^3}}{105\,b^3}.$

94. $\displaystyle \int \frac{\sqrt{a + bx}}{x}\, dx = 2 \sqrt{a + bx} + a \int \frac{dx}{x \sqrt{a + bx}}.$

95. $\displaystyle \int \frac{dx}{\sqrt{a + bx}} = \frac{2 \sqrt{a + bx}}{b}.$

96. $\displaystyle \int \frac{x\, dx}{\sqrt{a + bx}} = -\frac{2(2\,a - bx)}{3\,b^2} \sqrt{a + bx}.$

97. $\displaystyle \int \frac{x^2\, dx}{\sqrt{a + bx}} = \frac{2(8\,a^2 - 4\,abx + 3\,b^2x^2)}{15\,b^3} \sqrt{a + bx}.$

98. $\displaystyle \int \frac{dx}{x \sqrt{a + bx}} = \frac{1}{\sqrt{a}} \log \frac{\sqrt{a + bx} - \sqrt{a}}{\sqrt{a + bx} + \sqrt{a}},$

or $\displaystyle \frac{-2}{\sqrt{a}} \tanh^{-1} \frac{\sqrt{a + bx}}{\sqrt{a}},$ or $\displaystyle \frac{-2}{\sqrt{a}} \operatorname{ctnh}^{-1} \frac{\sqrt{a + bx}}{\sqrt{a}}$

99. $\displaystyle \int \frac{dx}{x \sqrt{a + bx}} = \frac{2}{\sqrt{-a}} \tan^{-1} \sqrt{\frac{a + bx}{-a}}.$

89. $\displaystyle \int \frac{dx}{(a' + b'x)^m X^n}$

$$= -\frac{1}{(m - 1)(ab'^2 - a'bb' + ca'^2)} \left(\frac{b'}{(a' + b'x)^{m-1} X^{n-1}} \right.$$

$$+ (m + n - 2)(bb' - 2\,ca') \int \frac{dx}{(a' + b'x)^{m-1} X^n}$$

$$\left. + (m + 2\,n - 3)\,c \int \frac{dx}{(a' + b'x)^{m-2} X^n} \right)$$

$$= \frac{1}{2(ab'^2 - a'bb' + ca'^2)} \left(\frac{-b'}{(n - 1)(a' + b'x)^{m-1} X^{n-1}} \right.$$

$$+ (2\,a'c - bb') \int \frac{dx}{(a' + b'x)^{m-1} X^n}$$

$$\left. + \frac{(m + 2\,n - 3)\,b'^2}{n - 1} \int \frac{dx}{(a' + b'x)^m X^{n-1}} \right).$$

If $ab'^2 - a'bb' + ca'^2 = 0$,

$$\int \frac{dx}{(a' + b'x)^m X^n}$$

$$= \frac{-1}{(m + n - 1)(bb' - 2\,a'c)} \left(\frac{b'}{(a' + b'x)^m X^{n-1}} \right.$$

$$\left. + (m + 2\,n - 2)\,c \int \frac{dx}{(a' + b'x)^{m-1} X^n} \right).$$

D. — Rational Fractions.

Every proper fraction can be represented by the general form :

$$\frac{f(x)}{F(x)} = \frac{g_1 x^{n-1} + g_2 x^{n-2} + g_3 x^{n-3} + \cdots + g_n}{x^n + k_1 x^{n-1} + k_2 x^{n-2} + \cdots + k_n}.$$

If a, b, c, etc., are the roots of the equation $F(x) = 0$, so that

$$F(x) = (x - a)^p (x - b)^q (x - c)^r \cdots,$$

then

$$\frac{f(x)}{F(x)} = \frac{A_1}{(x-a)^p} + \frac{A_2}{(x-a)^{p-1}} + \frac{A_3}{(x-a)^{p-2}} + \cdots + \frac{A_p}{x-a}$$

$$+ \frac{B_1}{(x-b)^q} + \frac{B_2}{(x-b)^{q-1}} + \frac{B_3}{(x-b)^{q-2}} + \cdots + \frac{B_q}{x-b}$$

$$+ \frac{C_1}{(x-c)^r} + \frac{C_2}{(x-c)^{r-1}} + \frac{C_3}{(x-c)^{r-2}} + \cdots + \frac{C_r}{x-c}$$

$$+ \quad \cdots \qquad \cdots \qquad \cdots \qquad \cdots \quad \cdots,$$

where the numerators of the separate fractions may be determined by the equations

$$A_m = \frac{\phi_1^{[m-1]}(a)}{(m-1)!}, \quad B_m = \frac{\phi_2^{[m-1]}(b)}{(m-1)!} \quad \text{etc., etc.}$$

$$\phi_1(x) = \frac{f(x)(x-a)^p}{F(x)}, \quad \phi_2(x) = \frac{f(x)(x-b)^q}{F(x)}, \quad \text{etc., etc.}$$

If a, b, c, etc., are single roots, then $p = q = r = \cdots = 1$, and

$$\frac{f(x)}{F(x)} = \frac{A}{x-a} + \frac{B}{x-b} + \frac{C}{x-c} \cdots$$

where $\quad A = \dfrac{f(a)}{F'(a)}, \quad B = \dfrac{f(b)}{F'(b)}$, etc.

The simpler fractions, into which the original fraction is thus divided, may be integrated by means of the formulas:

90. $\displaystyle\int \frac{h\,dx}{(mx+n)^l} = \int \frac{h\,d(mx+n)}{m(mx+n)^l} = \frac{h}{m(1-l)(mx+n)^{l-1}},$

and $\quad \displaystyle\int \frac{h\,dx}{mx+n} = \frac{h}{m} \log(mx+n).$

If any of the roots of the equation $f(x) = 0$ are imaginary the parts of the integral which arise from conjugate roots can be combined and the integral brought into a real form. The following formula, in which $i = \sqrt{-1}$, is often useful in combining logarithms of conjugate complex quantities:

$$\log(x \pm yi) = \tfrac{1}{2}\log(x^2 + y^2) \pm i \tan^{-1}\frac{y}{x}.$$

The identities given below are sometimes convenient:

$$\frac{1}{(a+bx^2)(a'+b'x^2)} \equiv \frac{1}{a'b - ab'} \cdot \left[\frac{b}{a+bx^2} - \frac{b'}{a'+b'x^2} \right],$$

$$\frac{m+nx}{(k+lx)(a+bx+cx^2)} \equiv \frac{1}{al^2 + ck^2 - bkl} \cdot$$
$$\left[\frac{l(ml-nk)}{k+lx} + \frac{c(nk-ml)x + (aln + ckm - blm)}{a+bx+cx^2} \right],$$

$$\frac{l+mx^n}{(a+bx^n)(a'+b'x^n)} \equiv \frac{1}{a'b - ab'} \cdot \left[\frac{bl-am}{a+bx^n} + \frac{a'm - b'l}{a'+b'x^n} \right].$$

$$\frac{1}{(x+a)(x+b)(x+c)} = \frac{A}{x+a} + \frac{B}{x+b} + \frac{C}{x+c},$$

where

$$A = \frac{1}{(a-b)(a-c)}, \quad B = \frac{1}{(b-c)(b-a)}, \quad C = \frac{1}{(c-a)(c-b)}.$$

$$\frac{1}{(x+a)(x+b)(x+c)(x+g)} = \frac{A}{x+a} + \frac{B}{x+b} + \frac{C}{x+c} + \frac{G}{x+g},$$

where

$$A = \frac{1}{(b-a)(c-a)(g-a)}, \quad B = \frac{1}{(a-b)(c-b)(g-b)}, \quad \text{etc.}$$

89. $\displaystyle\int \frac{dx}{(a' + b'x)^m X^n}$

$$= -\frac{1}{(m-1)(ab'^2 - a'bb' + ca'^2)}\left(\frac{b'}{(a' + b'x)^{m-1}X^{n-1}}\right.$$

$$+ (m + n - 2)(bb' - 2ca')\int \frac{dx}{(a' + b'x)^{m-1}X^n}$$

$$\left. + (m + 2n - 3)c\int \frac{dx}{(a' + b'x)^{m-2}X^n}\right)$$

$$= \frac{1}{2(ab'^2 - a'bb' + ca'^2)}\left(\frac{b'}{(n-1)(a' + b'x)^{m-1}X^{n-1}}\right.$$

$$+ (2a'c - bb')\int \frac{dx}{(a' + b'x)^{m-1}X^n}$$

$$\left. + \frac{(m + 2n - 3)b'^2}{n-1}\int \frac{dx}{(a' + b'x)^m X^{n-1}}\right).$$

If $ab'^2 - a'bb' + ca'^2 = 0$,

$$\int \frac{dx}{(a' + b'x)^m X^n}$$

$$= \frac{-1}{(m + n - 1)(bb' - 2a'c)}\left(\frac{b'}{(a' + b'x)^m X^{n-1}}\right.$$

$$\left. + (m + 2n - 2)c\int \frac{dx}{(a' + b'x)^{m-1}X^n}\right).$$

D. — RATIONAL FRACTIONS.

Every proper fraction can be represented by the general form :

$$\frac{f(x)}{F(x)} = \frac{g_1 x^{n-1} + g_2 x^{n-2} + g_3 x^{n-3} + \cdots + g_n}{x^n + k_1 x^{n-1} + k_2 x^{n-2} + \cdots + k_n}.$$

If a, b, c, etc., are the roots of the equation $F(x) = 0$, so that

$$F(x) = (x - a)^p (x - b)^q (x - c)^r \cdots,$$

then

$$\frac{f(x)}{F(x)} = \frac{A_1}{(x-a)^p} + \frac{A_2}{(x-a)^{p-1}} + \frac{A_3}{(x-a)^{p-2}} + \cdots + \frac{A_p}{x-a}$$

$$+ \frac{B_1}{(x-b)^q} + \frac{B_2}{(x-b)^{q-1}} + \frac{B_3}{(x-b)^{q-2}} + \cdots + \frac{B_q}{x-b}$$

$$+ \frac{C_1}{(x-c)^r} + \frac{C_2}{(x-c)^{r-1}} + \frac{C_3}{(x-c)^{r-2}} + \cdots + \frac{C_r}{x-c}$$

$$+ \cdots \qquad \cdots \qquad \cdots \qquad \cdots \qquad \cdots,$$

where the numerators of the separate fractions may be determined by the equations

$$A_m = \frac{\phi_1^{[m-1]}(a)}{(m-1)!}, \quad B_m = \frac{\phi_2^{[m-1]}(b)}{(m-1)!} \quad \text{etc., etc.}$$

$$\phi_1(x) = \frac{f(x)(x-a)^p}{F(x)}, \quad \phi_2(x) = \frac{f(x)(x-b)^q}{F(x)}, \quad \text{etc., etc.}$$

If a, b, c, etc., are single roots, then $p = q = r = \cdots = 1$, and

$$\frac{f(x)}{F(x)} = \frac{A}{x-a} + \frac{B}{x-b} + \frac{C}{x-c} \cdots$$

where $\qquad A = \frac{f(a)}{F'(a)}, \quad B = \frac{f(b)}{F'(b)}, \quad$ etc.

The simpler fractions, into which the original fraction is thus divided, may be integrated by means of the formulas:

90. $\int \frac{h\,dx}{(mx+n)^l} = \int \frac{h\,d(mx+n)}{m(mx+n)^l} = \frac{h}{m(1-l)(mx+n)^{l-1}},$

and $\qquad \int \frac{h\,dx}{mx+n} = \frac{h}{m} \log(mx+n).$

If any of the roots of the equation $f(x) = 0$ are imaginary, the parts of the integral which arise from conjugate roots can be combined and the integral brought into a real form. The following formula, in which $i = \sqrt{-1}$, is often useful in combining logarithms of conjugate complex quantities:

$$\log (x \pm yi) = \tfrac{1}{2} \log (x^2 + y^2) \pm i \tan^{-1} \frac{y}{x}.$$

The identities given below are sometimes convenient:

$$\frac{1}{(a + bx^2)(a' + b'x^2)} \equiv \frac{1}{a'b - ab'} \cdot \left[\frac{b}{a + bx^2} - \frac{b'}{a' + b'x^2} \right],$$

$$\frac{m + nx}{(k + lx)(a + bx + cx^2)} \equiv \frac{1}{al^2 + ck^2 - bkl} \cdot$$
$$\left[\frac{l(ml - nk)}{k + lx} + \frac{c(nk - ml)x + (aln + ckm - blm)}{a + bx + cx^2} \right],$$

$$\frac{l + mx^n}{(a + bx^n)(a' + b'x^n)} \equiv \frac{1}{a'b - ab'} \cdot \left[\frac{bl - am}{a + bx^n} + \frac{a'm - b'l}{a' + b'x^n} \right].$$

$$\frac{1}{(x + a)(x + b)(x + c)} = \frac{A}{x + a} + \frac{B}{x + b} + \frac{C}{x + c},$$

where

$$A = \frac{1}{(a - b)(a - c)}, \quad B = \frac{1}{(b - c)(b - a)}, \quad C = \frac{1}{(c - a)(c - b)}.$$

$$\frac{1}{(x + a)(x + b)(x + c)(x + g)} = \frac{A}{x + a} + \frac{B}{x + b} + \frac{C}{x + c} + \frac{G}{x + g};$$

where

$$A = \frac{1}{(b - a)(c - a)(g - a)}, \quad B = \frac{1}{(a - b)(c - b)(g - b)}, \text{ etc.}$$

III. IRRATIONAL ALGEBRAIC FUNCTIONS.

$$A. - \text{EXPRESSIONS INVOLVING } \sqrt{a + bx}.$$

The substitution of a new variable of integration, $y = \sqrt{a + bx}$, gives

91. $\int \sqrt{a + bx}\, dx = \frac{2}{3\, b} \sqrt{(a + bx)^3}.$

92. $\int x \sqrt{a + bx}\, dx = - \frac{2\,(2\, a - 3\, bx)\, \sqrt{(a + bx)^3}}{15\, b^2}.$

93. $\int x^2 \sqrt{a + bx}\, dx = \frac{2\,(8\, a^2 - 12\, abx + 15\, b^2 x^2)\, \sqrt{(a + bx)^3}}{105\, b^3}.$

94. $\int \frac{\sqrt{a + bx}}{x}\, dx = 2 \sqrt{a + bx} + a \int \frac{dx}{x \sqrt{a + bx}}.$

95. $\int \frac{dx}{\sqrt{a + bx}} = \frac{2 \sqrt{a + bx}}{b}.$

96. $\int \frac{x\, dx}{\sqrt{a + bx}} = - \frac{2\,(2\, a - bx)}{3\, b^2} \sqrt{a + bx}.$

97. $\int \frac{x^2\, dx}{\sqrt{a + bx}} = \frac{2\,(8\, a^2 - 4\, abx + 3\, b^2 x^2)}{15\, b^3} \sqrt{a + bx}.$

98. $\int \frac{dx}{x \sqrt{a + bx}} = \frac{1}{\sqrt{a}} \log \frac{\sqrt{a + bx} - \sqrt{a}}{\sqrt{a + bx} + \sqrt{a}},$

or $\frac{-2}{\sqrt{a}} \tanh^{-1} \frac{\sqrt{a + bx}}{\sqrt{a}},$ or $\frac{-2}{\sqrt{a}} \operatorname{ctnh}^{-1} \frac{\sqrt{a + bx}}{\sqrt{a}}$

99. $\int \frac{dx}{x \sqrt{a + bx}} = \frac{2}{\sqrt{-a}} \tan^{-1} \sqrt{\frac{a + bx}{-a}}.$